Valuable Garden Weeds

CHRIS HOWKINS

PUBLISHED BY
Chris Howkins,   70, Grange Road, New Haw, Addlestone,
                 Surrey. KT15 3RH

PRINTED BY
Unwin Brothers Ltd, The Gresham Press, Old Woking,
                 Surrey, England. GU22 9LH

ISBN
0 9509105 9 7

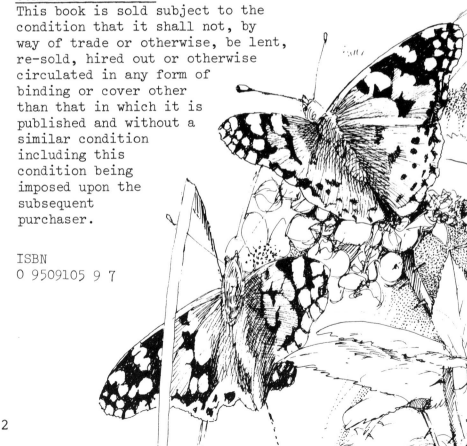

PROVIDENCE
has made the most useful things
the most common
and for that reason
we neglect them ;

wrote the apothecary, Nicholas
Culpeper, back in the 17th century. If he thought
we were neglecting common weeds then, how high he
would fling his arms in despair now!

Everyday plants had everyday uses from providing food
and medicines to dyes and raw materials, and were
valued for that very fact. Most have been superceded
by factory produce but some, especially medicinal ones,
are being reviewed afresh. Thus Feverfew and Evening
Primroses are enjoying a revival.

DO NOT try folk medicines for yourselves. The active
ingredients can vary from plant to plant, place to place,
year to year, not to mention the differing sensitivities
we each have to such things. Some people can't eat
strawberries or mushrooms while others relish them.
The plants can have changed too - Rhubarb was introduced
as a green vegetable long before its leaves developed
today's level of toxicity. Turnips are poisonous if they
are left standing in their cooking water. TAKE CARE.

References to "Martindale" are to his 'Extra Pharmacopoeia'
(28th Ed.); the standard reference to the world's drugs.
Place names are in Surrey.

Those tiresome opportunists that invade our gardens and
get condemned as weeds have fascinating tales to tell..
..but remember....if liars eat the roots of Couch Grass
while singing the right words, then the rest of us will
believe what they say!

BRUISEWORT

Daisy
Bellis perennis

There are over
13,000 different
daisies. They form
the largest family
of flowering plants
and range from trees
down to the lowly
little herb that is loved from
childhood memories of making daisy
chains.

In the 14th century the Clerk of the King's Works tending
the royal manor of Byfleet was Geoffrey Chaucer, famous
for his "Canterbury Tales". He declared:-

> "Of all the flowers in the mead,
>   Then love I most the flowers, white and red,
>   Such as men call daisies in our town."

He would notice the name. Daisy was the traditional
Saxon one whereas at Court he would have heard
the French name used - Marguerite. They
were the emblem of St.Margaret, patron
saint of herbalists, and also of
Margaret of Anjou, wife of Henry VI,
buried at Chertsey Abbey, and of
Margaret Beaufort, Lady of
the Manor of Woking and
mother of Henry VII.
The Beaufort daisies
were special. They
were double - the
first record of
such things.

Sir James Berners kneeling in prayer in the medieval stained glass at West Horsley would have known the daisy as an all-purpose medicine. The leaves were compounded into an ointment for all external injuries, hence its old name of Bruisewort. A suggested origin for the generic name Bellis is from Bellum - war. Daisies grew on medieval battle fields; more likely it records the collection of daisies after a battle for use by surgeons like Sir Thomas Morsted of Betchworth. He led the twelve surgeons who served Henry V on his French campaigns of Agincourt fame.

Distilled water of the whole plant, including the roots, was used widely for all sorts of internal ailings. Thus in the 16th century Gerard recommended it for "alle the inwarde parts" and it was still being recommended at the end of the 18th century. Nowadays its bitter leaves (tannic acid) have ceased to be used even in salads. Back in 1699 Sir John Evelyn recorded that "The young roots are frequently eaten by the Spaniards and the Italians all the Spring till June."

Today this valuable herb is despised as a weed of lawns. An old Surrey gardener can remember from his youth the day 'the Master' lined up all the garden staff while he paced the lawns until he found the one and only daisy he had spotted from an upper window. The lawnsman was sacked and given the daisy instead of his wages. There were 14 acres of lawns.

Cover seven daisies with one foot and it is the first day of summer, (nine in Surrey if you have big feet!).

DOG GRASS

Couch Grass
Hist. Agropyrum repens
curr. Elymus repens

Dog in the name of plants
indicates usually that they are
the common ones, like Dog Rose and Dog Daisy.
When it comes to Dog Grass, however, it records the way
animals, like cats and dogs, seek out the
grass to eat when they have an
upset stomach. The hairy leaves
cause them to vomit; the act
is not due to poisons in
the grass.

Dog Grass
is the dreaded
Couch Grass or Twitch
to gardeners. Its gentle
healing properties have been
forgotten but in the 17th century
Culpeper wrote that, "Although the
gardener be of another opinion, yet
the physician holds half an acre of them
to be worth five acres of carrots twice
told over." It is still listed in Martindale
today and its usage is recorded as far back as
the Ancient Greeks. The generic name, Agropyrum,
is Greek for 'field wheat' and it is related closely
to the bread wheats in commercial
production today. In the past
bread has been made from the
roots of this grass. The Saxons
noted the way the creeping roots
invade loose soil and named it
'civice', meaning full of life,
and from this, it is thought,
derives the name Couch.

6

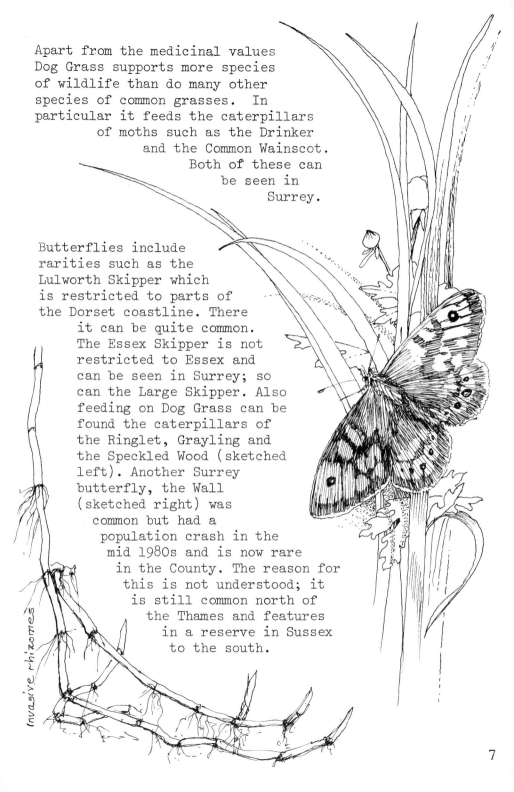

Apart from the medicinal values
Dog Grass supports more species
of wildlife than do many other
species of common grasses. In
particular it feeds the caterpillars
        of moths such as the Drinker
            and the Common Wainscot.
                Both of these can
                    be seen in
                        Surrey.

Butterflies include
rarities such as the
Lulworth Skipper which
is restricted to parts of
the Dorset coastline. There
        it can be quite common.
        The Essex Skipper is not
        restricted to Essex and
        can be seen in Surrey; so
        can the Large Skipper. Also
        feeding on Dog Grass can be
        found the caterpillars of
        the Ringlet, Grayling and
        the Speckled Wood (sketched
        left). Another Surrey
        butterfly, the Wall
        (sketched right) was
            common but had a
            population crash in the
            mid 1980s and is now rare
            in the County. The reason for
            this is not understood; it
            is still common north of
                the Thames and features
                in a reserve in Sussex
                to the south.

Invasive rhizomes

DUTCH CLOVER

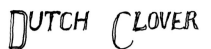

Creeping Clover
Trifolium repens

Clover in the lawn has tiny
leaves that go unnoticed –
until a drought turns the grass
brown and then the Clover triumphs in
its vibrant green. In meadows it is a
taller plant with larger leaves. It
also makes a good garden plant but only
if you confine it to a pot or trough on
the patio. It will trail its
white-flowered stems over for a
long period but be wise – cut off
every faded head!

It is the flower of Olwen in Welsh
mythology. Her name means 'white
way' and refers to the carpet
of white flowers that sprang
up wherever her feet passed.
It is also the flower of
honey fame because it
has shorter flower tubes
than some Clovers and
that suits the short
tongue of the honey
bee.

Clover is important in pastures, for adding protein to the hay and nitrogen to the soil. Fortunately it is not toxic, at least not in Britain but in some parts of the world this is not the case. Toxins arise sometimes from fungi infecting the plant rather than from the clover itself. Why this does not happen in Britain is not understood clearly; a number of factors are involved.

The plant played an important part in early agricultural improvement schemes although the species of clover, or honeysuckle as it was then called, is not always clear but the first reference to RED clover being used is by Sir Richard Weston of Sutton Place near Guildford in 1645. He is attributed with bringing the WHITE clover into cultivation along with other ideas gathered from his travels in the Low Countries, hence the white or creeping clover is still called Dutch Clover.

By the 1960s British clover had fallen from favour due to unpredictable yields. By 1985 a new 'cocktail' of four strains called 'Ensign' was being promoted. One of the strains was called Olwen although it originated in S.W.France. Another, called Menna, came from an intensively stocked cow pasture in Surrey where it had proved itself particularly durable.

GROUNDSEL

Senecio vulgaris

Groundsel is a very variable weed.
Those of you with dry sandy soil
like mine will have weedy little
specimens like those picked for
drawing while those of you with a
richer deeper soil will have robust
Groundsels.

The very name is Saxon. It
was called Grundeswilge or Grundeswelge
which has been explained as 'ground
swallower', referring to the
speed with which it can cover
freshly disturbed soil. It
has been estimated that one plant
can give rise to another million.

Some etymologists doubt this
interpretation and forward
the meaning of 'puss swallower'
from its days as a healing herb.
The Saxons chopped its
leaves into a poultice
to draw out the puss from
septic wounds. It has
been used also to
sooth the gums of
teething infants.

Today its only use seems
to be to pop a sprig in with
a cage bird. It is not listed
in Martindale but seven other
members of the genus are - the
ragworts, which are poisonous,
causing liver problems.

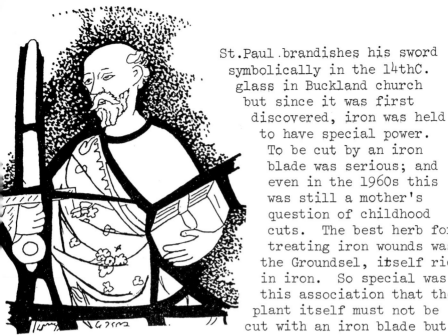

St.Paul brandishes his sword
symbolically in the 14thC.
glass in Buckland church
but since it was first
discovered, iron was held
to have special power.
To be cut by an iron
blade was serious; and
even in the 1960s this
was still a mother's
question of childhood
cuts. The best herb for
treating iron wounds was
the Groundsel, itself rich
in iron. So special was
this association that the
plant itself must not be
cut with an iron blade but
be picked or pulled up. The smell from the broken roots
is said to cure certain types of headache. Perhaps
the little Saxon pot in Weybridge Museum
held precious herbs and medicines; we'll
never know.

Groundsel was used to relieve
scrofula (type of T.B.) in the absence
of the Royal Touch. Edward the
Confessor 'touched' Saxon sufferers and
the practice continued until the reign
of Queen Anne. It was Henry VII who
created a special ceremony and who
introduced the gold 'touchpiece' token.
Thousands of desperate sufferers were
attracted to the ceremonies; between
1660 and 1664 Charles II touched
nearly 24,000 of his loyal subjects.
People from Witley hired a coach to
take them to London to join the long
queues for what Pepys thought was
"an ugly office". The Groundsel cure
couldn't have been very effective!

PASSERINA

Chickweed
Stellaria media

In the early 1930s
you could still buy
a wild British song
bird for a cage.
They were bought in a
brown paper bag from a
street trader. The birds
suffered dreadfully from
the manner and moment of
their capture through to their
sale, before which they were tortured to make them sing.
This trade was abolished through the efforts of the
Parker family of Hambledon. Eric Parker, as Editor of
The Field, sent out reporters and photographers in secret
and published their findings. The outcry was such that
their lives were threatened by the traders. At Hambledon
the rest of the family worked to the same end through the
National Federation of Women's Institutes and in 1933 his
daughter addressed the National Conference in the Albert
Hall on this subject. The 8,000 delegates then passed
unanimously the Hambledon Resolution calling for changes
in the law. Later that year a Bill was adopted by the
Government and protective legislation was achieved.

In the 16th century our little perching or 'passerine'
birds were just as popular. Gerard records that the
chickweed was fed to such birds as the Linnet (illus.)
when they were pining for their freedom
and refusing to eat anything else.
It revived them and for this
reason the birdmen called
the plant 'passerina'.
It was fed also to
poultry and their chicks
as a valuable supplement;
it contains phosphorus, iron,
copper and potassium. Thus,
whether eaten fresh in salads or
cooked like spinach, it does good.
Although it is a member of the
Carnation family (Caryophyllaceae)
and therefore contains saponins, it
does not seem to harm humans.
The dried and fresh leaves
have been used in ointments
and poultices for piles,
sores and scurvy. The
juice or cooking water
has been used for eye
and skin care and as
a laxative.

Gardeners hate
weeding out a
mat of chickweed
because it traps
water. A line of
white hairs spirals
down the stem to swop
sides between the nodes
and these hairs stop the
raindrops running through.
Oddly, chickweed does not
like rain. It closes up
its flowers and seed pods
and bends them downwards if
rain threatens. At the same
time it clasps its top leaves over
the growing tip. On good days the
flowers open at nine o'clock in the
morning and remain open for twelve hours.

PEWTERWORT

Horsetail
Equisetum arvense

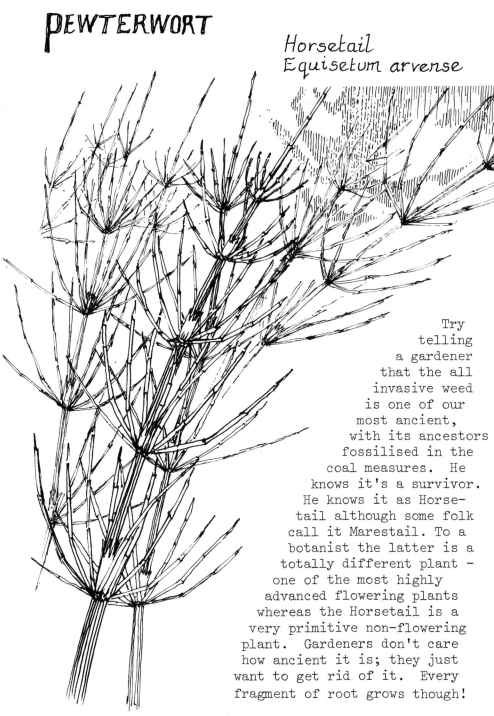

Try
telling
a gardener
that the all
invasive weed
is one of our
most ancient,
with its ancestors
fossilised in the
coal measures. He
knows it's a survivor.
He knows it as Horse-
tail although some folk
call it Marestail. To a
botanist the latter is a
totally different plant –
one of the most highly
advanced flowering plants
whereas the Horsetail is a
very primitive non-flowering
plant. Gardeners don't care
how ancient it is; they just
want to get rid of it. Every
fragment of root grows though!

The persistent Horsetail has tough
stems that feel gritty. This is
because the plant absorbs and stores
large amounts of silica. This has
made it valuable for bones and teeth,
hair and nails, but also gave it a
totally different, non herbal, use; it
served as an early form of 'sandpaper'.
The cabinet makers took large amounts and
for really big jobs were pleased to get
the Giant Horsetail, Equisetum telmateia,
with stems up to 2m long. The Common Horsetail, Equisetum arvense, at a mere 80cm max.
was quite sufficient for the fletcher polishing
his arrows and for the pewterer (hence one common
name being pewterwort).

In the home it was just as valuable. In the days before
commercial pot scourers, detergents, hot running water,
and easy-clean surfaces, the washing-up was an ordeal.
The Horsetail was ideal for scouring pots, being tough
and gritty and well able to trap all the muck in its
little branchlets. Then it could be thrown away with
no more ado. Water was not even needed because the
pot was finished off with a handful of ashes from the
hearth. They were sterile and the potash content acted
as soap. Girl Guides still do this at camp but are not
often aware that this is the time honoured method of
washing-up without water. Water was always scarce in
many of the heathland communities and any chalkland
homes high above the spring line.

In the past it has been eaten as a vegetable in desperate
times but this shouldn't be revived as Horsetails
contain the enzyme thiaminase which destroys vitamin
B_1; poisoning of farm animals is rare but watch for it
in hay as the drying does not destroy the toxicity. As a
herb it has been valued, for its healing and powerful
styptic qualities as well as being antiseptic and a
disinfectant. A garden fungicide can be made from it
too. There is still a small entry for it in Martindale
where there is reference to its value in treating some
respiratory disorders but there is also the warning
about those toxic alkaloids. Best use it as sandpaper!

RUN-BY-THE-GROUND

Mints, such as *Mentha Pulegium*
Pennyroyal

Some of the most irritating weeds are
those first planted as desirable plants
but which have since run amok.
Mint is supreme at this.

From the few species first grown
there are now over 600 different
cultivars as they hybridize so
readily. All had a wide range
of uses but none more so than
Pennyroyal, Mentha pulegium.
Its name does not come from
'sovereign cure' as so often
stated but from 'pulegium'
which was used originally
for the fleabanes.

A prime virtue of mints was
in the treatment of water.
Village pumps and garden
wells harboured disease
and death which was known
long before germs were
identified. Home brews of
ale, beer and cider were
safer as they were too acid
for germs to live in. For
water, there were steeping
herbs, like mint. Not only
did the aromatic oil disguise
the odour and the taste but
it contained a natural antiseptic and aided the digestive
system.

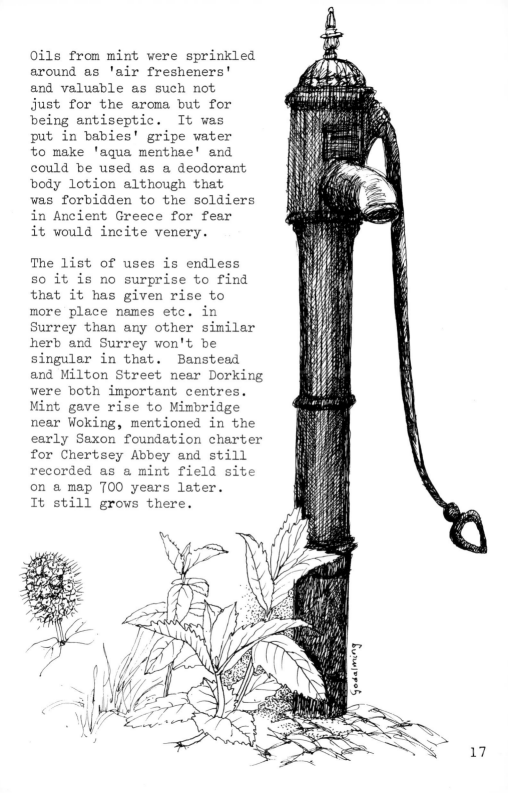

Oils from mint were sprinkled around as 'air fresheners' and valuable as such not just for the aroma but for being antiseptic. It was put in babies' gripe water to make 'aqua menthae' and could be used as a deodorant body lotion although that was forbidden to the soldiers in Ancient Greece for fear it would incite venery.

The list of uses is endless so it is no surprise to find that it has given rise to more place names etc. in Surrey than any other similar herb and Surrey won't be singular in that. Banstead and Milton Street near Dorking were both important centres. Mint gave rise to Mimbridge near Woking, mentioned in the early Saxon foundation charter for Chertsey Abbey and still recorded as a mint field site on a map 700 years later. It still grows there.

17

SHEPHERD'S PURSE
Capsella bursa-pastoris

Gardeners - don't destroy this weed.
Don't pull it up or cut it down; just
leave it to seed wildly wherever possible.
It will repay your kindness by destroying
garden pests like thrips and eelworms.
It eats them. The Shepherd's Purse is
one of the country's least known carnivorous
plants.

The seeds are coated with a sticky
glue of tasty carbohydrate which swells
with moisture and releases aromas to attract
tiny creepy-crawlies like the thrips and
the eelworms. When they try to eat the
seed they stick to it. Then they find that
the glue contains two corrosive acids to
destroy them and two digestive enzymes
capable of dissolving protein.
Soon the prey is reduced to
liquid and absorbed by the
seed, leaving any hard shell
behind. The seeds are soon
growing happily after their
protein-rich meal, no
matter how poor is the
soil.

Other weeds can do the
same and are being
investigated in the
search for a 'safe'
natural insecticide.

Leave as much of
this plant as you
can for a garden
free from pests.

Of Shepherd's Purse Culpeper wrote that "few plants possess greater virtues than this and yet it is utterly disregarded." That was three and a half centuries ago and the puny weed is no more highly regarded now. Only during World War I did Germany turn again to this herb of ancient practice but only because the more modern medicines had become unobtainable. What they needed was a styptic - something that would stop bleeding - and for this the Shepherd's Purse has always been esteemed. It can be used externally for bleeding wounds and it can be turned into a medicine that when drunk will stop internal bleeding. This was not a very pleasant medicine as the plant belongs to the same family as cresses and mustard so the strong taste has to be disguised. At least it works. When so many ailments can result in bleeding it is no surprise to find Shepherd's Purse being recommended for a long list of them.

Nothing is perfect. This herb may be of value to the gardener and the herbalist but the farmer has to be more wary. If dairy cattle feed upon an abundance of the plant their is a danger that its strong taste will taint the milk. Similarly, the poultry farmer knows that wild birds flock down onto the seeding heads but that if his poultry consume too much then the flavour of the eggs will be increased, perhaps by too much. The colour of them darkens too.

This is a really tough plant. From Europe people have taken it all round the world where it seems to adapt to all new conditions. So tough is it that pollen analysis has shown that it persisted in Britain through the last Ice Age.

ST ANTHONY'S TURNIP

Bulbous Buttercup
Ranunculus bulbosus

Buttercups are wonderful yellow
flowers that children hold under
the chins of their friends to see
if a golden glow is reflected upon
the skin. If it is, then that is a
sure indication that the child likes
butter. George Sturt, recalling his
early Victorian childhood in Farnham,
in "Small Boy in the Sixties", played
the game and children do still. It is
harmless enough. The Buttercups are not.

Their sap is bitter with toxins of the
proto-anemonin group which cause the
skin to blister and in this was found
a value. Rheumatic wrists and gouty
feet were blistered and ulcerated
deliberately with buttercup juice
to give relief by causing a
counter-irritant.

Just as drastic was the way the
beggars used it to cause running
sores, the better to induce
sympathetic donations. They
thereby risked being
shunned for having
leprosy.

Cuckoo Buds
Goldie Buds

20

Cattle avoid eating Buttercups except when food is scarce and then they can develop quite a liking for them, with unfortunate results. In hay, however, Buttercups are safe because the drying destroys the toxins.

It is said dairymen rubbed Buttercups into cows' udders on May Day to promote production but no cow is going to stand by and have her udder blistered! Perhaps the plant was rubbed in, without shedding the sap, to leave a bitter taste that would encourage calves to wean and leave more milk for man. On Midsummer's Eve cows were garlanded with Buttercups to bless the milk.

The most favoured Buttercup was the Bulbous - the one with reflexed sepals and a swollen base to the stem, like a small turnip. Eating those causes a burning in the mouth such as suffered by St. Anthony (from a different cause) so children were warned against St. Anthony's Turnips. Ingestion by children causes vomiting before damage is done and so only one child fatality has been traced.

Early herbalists warned of its dire action and refrained from publishing the usages. Gerard stressed a "most exquisite moderation, with a most exact and due manner of tempering", and that is how it is used in homoeopathy today.

STINGING NETTLE

Urtica dioica

"Nettles are so well known that they need no description; they may be found, by feeling, in the darkest night," wrote Culpeper with undoubted accuracy. They creep quietly into the garden from under the fence and hide maliciously behind the shed. They engulf anything interesting that an artist might like to draw, such as this old wheel and churn.

Of all the weeds in this book most space has been allocated to the nettle because it is the most valuable of all. It was formerly harvested and sold off in markets to raise extra income; sold for food, for fibre and for medicine.

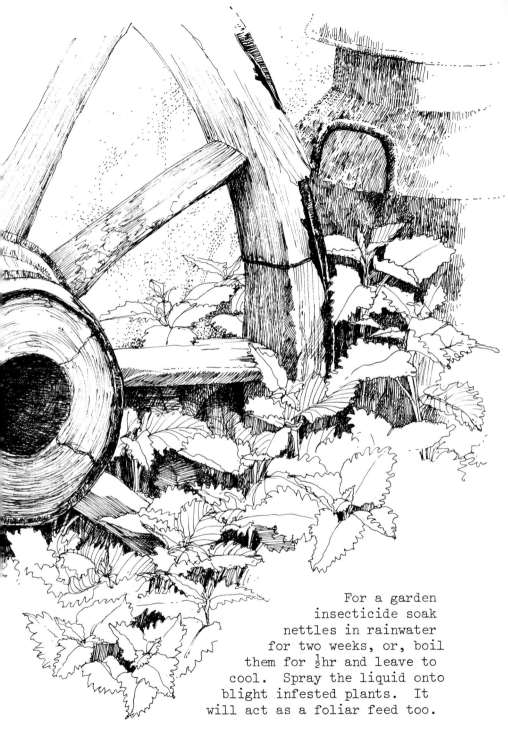

For a garden
insecticide soak
nettles in rainwater
for two weeks, or, boil
them for $\frac{1}{2}$hr and leave to
cool. Spray the liquid onto
blight infested plants. It
will act as a foliar feed too.

Tough old
nettles have
a name of uncertain
origin. It is
thought to derive
from the Saxon for
needle or for net –
both referring to its
fibre qualities.

These were utilised by
the Germans in the First
World War when they had
to resort to using nettle
fibres as a substitute for
cotton. Nettle stems yield
fibres of varying values according
to their degree of maturity; the
very best produce a cloth rated as
good as linen. They have been used
for cloth and rope since prehistoric
times, and later, for paper. Thus scything
down nettles is an ancient job but an important
one since the crop could be sold or bartered in the local
market; this source of income was not overlooked by the
nobles on their great estates.

Nettles still have potential for the textile industry.
It all needs further research. People cannot agree, for
example, on the best way to extract the fibres.
Much to everyone's surprise the invasive nettle
proved temperamental under cultivation, and so
in poor countries where they are still used
it is the wild nettle beds that are harvested.

The by-products from processing are also of
value. Nettle juice soothes burns and aids
healing. It can be used as a coagulent to
stop nose-bleeds and to seal leaking joints
in wooden sinks, utensils, etc. It can be
used as a substitute for rennet for curdling
milk, it can be burned in oil lamps, it can
flavour beer and provide green/grey/yellow dye.

Nettle leaves are
still steamed as
a vegetable but
only the young
shoots should
be used and
only in some
moderation.
They are rich in proteins, fibre,
vitamins and minerals, acting as a
tonic but with a slight laxative action.
Nettle tea is diuretic, astringent and an
aid to digestion. The astringent qualities
led to their use in bathwater, hair lotions
and face creams for spots and sunburn.

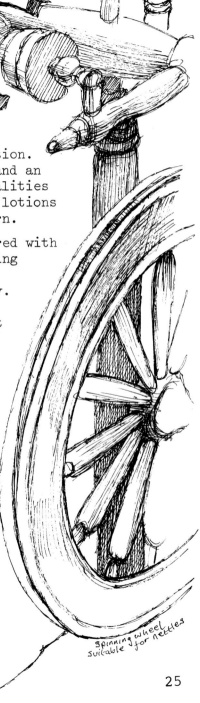

The burn of nettle stings can be cured with
their own juice - an unlikely sounding
solution but one discovered by the
ancients as it is described by Pliny.
The sting is not due to formic acid
as was once believed (only the first
reaction) but to histamine, acetyl-
chlorine and 5-hydroxytryptamine
which is serotonin, important in
the nervous system and migraines.
The stings are well known as a
counter-irritant for rheumatism.
They can be cured by rubbing
them with antidotes in leaves
of docks, balm, mint, rhubarb,
rosemary and sage.

Countrymen claim that nettles
grown under fruit trees not
only hasten ripening but also
promote larger fruit. Apples
were stored on layers of nettle
leaves and plums retain their
bloom if wrapped in nettle leaves.

Wonderful things stinging nettles!

spinning wheel
suitable for nettles

BUTTERFLIES AND NETTLES

Red Admirals

Whereas most of the weeds in this book have lost their value, the nettle is enjoying a revival with wildlife gardeners. It is the main source of food for the caterpillars of the Peacock, Comma, Small Tortoiseshell and Red Admiral butterflies.

Relegating the nettle patch to a shady corner does not work. For best results the nettles need to be in a warm, sunny, sheltered location. For Small Tortoiseshells cut the nettles to ground level in the second week of June so females can lay eggs on new growth that will feed the larvae best. Leave some nettles for the other species.

The size of the nettle patch is not crucial but 9 x 3 ft is recommended.

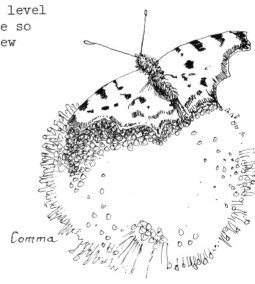

Comma

The various species of butterfly that utilise the nettles for laying eggs do so throughout the summer so it is important to maintain the nettle patch over a period of at least five months.

The Small Tortoiseshell starts in late March or early April and is followed by the Peacock in May with the Comma and Red Admiral following on from late July.

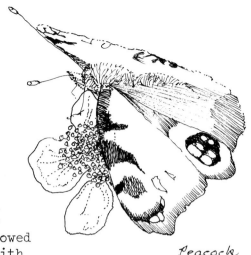

Peacock

Small
Tortoiseshell

AND
MOTHS
Scarlet Tiger
Bright-line Brown-eye
Green Silver Line
Snout
Small Magpie.

WAYBREAD

Broad-leaved Plantain
Plantago major

One of the nine sacred herbs of the
Anglo-Saxons was the plantain that
plonks flat rosettes of leaves into
our lawns. We call it Broad-leaved
Plantain but the Saxons called it
Weybroed or Weg Broade meaning the
plant of the broad way or roadside.
It still flourishes in such places,
having developed a number of adaptations
to suit such a hostile habitat. Such strong
characteristics were always noted and taken as
a sign from God that the plant would have healing
virtues for conditions related to those characteristics
in some way. Thus the Weybroed was used to cool and
sooth the sore feet of travellers upon the broadway.
Later, reapers found that it was just as good
for soothing sore and blistered hands at the
beginning of the harvest season before their
skin hardened.

As the Saxon languages declined so did
the understanding of the name and it
became corrupted into WayBREAD.
People tried eating it, no
doubt chopping it first
as the leaves have
very tough fibres.

28

When it comes to eating this tough old weed it proves
to be nutritious. It is a source of calcium, potassium,
and sulphur. More importantly it contains vitamin K
which is needed for blood clotting and for this reason
it was used widely as a wound herb. The large leaves
were used as a styptic poultice - remember that although
the leaves of the rosettes on the lawn tend to be small,
the leaves of wayside plants often reach 15cm and can
reach 30cm. Small leaves or pieces of leaf were rubbed
into stings and bites;not only is the leaf cooling but
it has antibiotic properties. These same antibiotic
properties have led to the use of the plant in potions
and teas etc. for internal infections.

All in all Waybread was a
vital ingredient of many
country cure-all
ointments.

It is the value of
the seeds that keeps
the herb in use today.
According to Martindale they can
be used as a substitute for ispaghula which is
another plantain (Plantago ovata). The seeds
are certainly popular with wild birds, especially
the goldfinches; whole charms of them often rise
from the roadsides where they have been feeding.
Gardeners - have no fear of this weed in the lawn
because every seven years they will turn into little
birds and fly off to mate with cuckoos!

WET-A-BED

Dandelion
Taraxacum officinale

So valuable has been the Dandelion that a whole book could be filled.

The generic name Taraxacum comes from the Greek 'taraxos' disorder and 'akos' remedy. The specific name officinale refers to its official use as a medicine. It makes good medicines without toxicity.

The Arabs, the great physicians of the early Middle Ages, were extolling its virtues in the 9th century and soon it was adopted by the Europeans who called it Dent-de-lion, the teeth of the lion, referring to the reflexed teeth of the leaves. Every part of the plant can be used.

As a child I was paid 3d per bucket for the flowers by the wine makers. Not only does the wine encourage the partaking of another glass but stimulates the whole bodily system, especially the kidneys, hence the various names referring to bed-wetting. The flowers make a good cosmetic wash.

The stem juice is a white latex that stains skin brown
but when prepared properly can be used in facial creams
and cosmetics without a staining problem. Used neat it
was dabbed on warts to remove them and is said to be
good for spots.

The leaves, shredded, make tasty sandwiches
although old leaves need the midrib
removing. They can be added to
salads or cooked with greens.
By Victorian times a more
delicate flavour was needed
and so "The Beeton Book of
Garden Management" gives
directions for blanching
them like chicory.
Then they provide
a fine late-winter
salad, rich in
vitamins A and C,
calcium, iron,
magnesium, potassium
and silica.

Then there are the
roots, which are best when
two years old. They are lifted
usually between September and February
although growers debate when is 'best'.
Some leave them until July if a hot taste
is required. They can be chopped for sprinkling
on salads or dried and powdered for medicinal use and as
a caffeine-free substitute for coffee. They are good for
inlammations like rheumatism and gout and are a laxative.

Old Bettesworth told George Sturt of Farnham at the end
of last century that he roasted Dandelion roots in the
oven and carried them in his pocket to help him control
contrary horses. If only that worked for other people
just think what fun could be had at the Horse of the
Year Show or a Race Meeting!!

According to Culpepper Dandelions cure hypochondriacs!

INDEX OF PLANT NAMES (first page of entry)

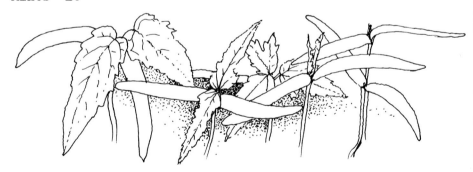

IN THE SAME SERIES : "Plants to Celebrate Midwinter"

FOR A LIST OF OTHER PUBLICATIONS AND TALKS GIVEN TO GROUPS WRITE TO

Chris Howkins, 70 Grange Road, New Haw, Surrey. KT15 3RH